Lightning McQueen

Sally

STARRING

Mater

Chick Hicks

Doc

First published by Parragon in 2009
Parragon
Queen Street House
4 Queen Street
Bath BA1 1HE, UK

ISBN 978-1-4075-3229-5
Printed in China

Bath · New York · Singapore · Hong Kong · Cologne · Delhi · Melbourne

"Pit stop! Pit stop!" cried Guido as he zoomed over and joined the gang at Flo's café.

The little forklift buzzed with excitement. Would his friend Lightning McQueen win the Piston Cup?

Earlier that week, McQueen had accidentally found himself in Radiator Springs on his way to the tie-breaker race in California. He had to work hard in Radiator Springs, but he also made lots of friends. Now, everyone in Radiator Springs was sad that McQueen was gone . . . but also excited about his big race.

"Do you think he can beat Chick Hicks?" wondered Sally. "I hear Chick is one mean racecar."

"McQueen can beat anybody, I know it!" said Mater. McQueen and Mater had become best friends in a very short time.

Mater believed in McQueen, **one hundred percent!**

They watched a car with a bright green paint job fill the TV screen. It was McQueen's rival, Chick Hicks!

"McQueen? Why should I worry about him?" Chick's voice came through the TV speaker. "He ended up in some rusty little town, playing with tractors and taking Sunday drives. He's not serious about winning. But I am!"

Everybody knew Chick Hicks never played fair. In fact, he caused bad accidents. In his garage, Doc saw a glint of gold through the dust and clutter. It was one of his Piston Cup trophies, the last one he earned before a devastating crash ended his racing career. He realized that he didn't want an accident like that to happen to anybody.

"McQueen's not really such a bad guy," he thought. "He just needs a good team behind him, especially if he's going to avoid Chick's dirty tricks."

Yes, McQueen needed a team, whether he knew it or not.

"Listen up, everybody," Doc's voice boomed down the main street from Flo's all the way to Sally's motel. "The rookie needs our help. He's out there with no pit crew and two tough opponents. I'm not going to let Lightning McQueen lose just because he thinks he can do it all on his own. Who's with me?"

Everybody was, of course!

Luigi and Guido got to work choosing some tyres. Lightning McQueen would need some good ones.

By morning the crew was inside the stadium. What a feeling it was, to be surrounded by all that excitement! But the Radiator Springs crew had a job to do.

"Pit stop!" said Guido when he saw all the pitties and their tool racks. As soon as Mater unhooked him, he rolled over to a spot to set up.

Sarge took command when he saw the orderly layout of the pit lane and the precise actions of the racing teams.

"You, Flo, over here," he ordered. "Guido, we need the tyres right there."

Ramone had something else in mind, "Hey, Doc! Let me give you a paint job. You gotta let these folks know that you're an important car".

"Not me," said Doc. "Try snazzing-up this pit instead. We need to show off our star car, not me."

Doc drove over to the other side of the track to check out the other crews. But as he neared Chick Hicks' tent he overheard something bad – really bad.

"I'm not gonna let anyone get in the way of me winning that race today," Chick said to his crew. "If I have to, I'll make The King and that rookie wipe out so fast their tyres won't even spin."

Doc peeked in and saw Chick turn and wink to his crew. "The Cup is mine, boys," said Chick.

Doc felt his oil heat up. He couldn't stand for this! It was time to help McQueen, even if it took his last drop of fuel. Could he find McQueen in time to warn him about Chick's evil plans? Doc returned so fast to the group that he almost overheated.

"This is what friendship is all about," thought Doc as Ramone finished painting him. "We are all a family."

And then, as a high-octane boost rushed through him, he climbed the crew-chief platform – with Ramone's blazing letters freshly painted on his side: Number 51, The Fabulous Hudson Hornet.

"Look, it's the Hudson Hornet!" cried a car in the stands.

The crowd roared and cheered, louder and louder. Everywhere, Doc saw a sea of flashing headlights and flying antenna balls. They were cheering for him!

Doc was too focused on the upcoming race to smile. But it was clear – Doc Hudson was proud to be back, and it felt good to hear the crowds roaring their approval.

It was all so exciting that no one in the crowd really cared when Chick Hicks was announced the winner of the tiebreaker race.

Instead, they cheered for McQueen as he helped The King cross the finish line. They cheered as they watched McQueen cruise on over to his crew chief, Doc, the Hudson Hornet.

Yes, indeed, the crowd cheered for the real winners of this race: Lightning McQueen and his Radiator Springs family.

Back in Radiator Springs, everybody gathered at Flo's to hear about the race.

"Doc and I want to build a racing headquarters near the town," McQueen told Sally.

Doc nodded. "It will be a special design – a first-class track that won't spoil our beautiful desert landscape."

"A great idea," said Sally. "And it will put Radiator Springs back on the map."

It wasn't long before Radiator Springs became an international racing sensation. Doc and McQueen sent invitations to race cars all over the world. They came to the town to share tips and techniques on how to become better racers.